RECITAL REPERTOIRE
FOR CELLISTS

Selected and edited by Julian Lloyd Webber and Simon Nicholls
for Cello and Piano · Book One

FABER *ff* MUSIC

Preface

The 12 pieces included in the two volumes of *Recital Repertoire for Cellists* follow on naturally from *The Young Cellist's Repertoire* Book 3. Now the emphasis is on performance, and we hope that in addition to their value for teaching, these works may prove useful as alternatives to more traditional recital material.

Once again, a wide variety of styles is represented in each volume, ranging from the Baroque era to the 20th century, and the selection has been made as much for musical as for technical content.

Wherever possible the text is based on original sources, but the realisations from figured bass and the fingerings and bowings in the solo part are the responsibility of the editors.

JULIAN LLOYD WEBBER
SIMON NICHOLLS

© 1987 by Faber Music Ltd
First published in 1987 by Faber Music Ltd
3 Queen Square London WC1N 3AU
Music engraved by Allan Hill
Printed in England by Caligraving Ltd
All rights reserved

ISBN 0-571-50793-X

To buy Faber Music publications or to find out about the full range of titles available
please contact your local music retailer or Faber Music sales enquiries:

Faber Music Limited, Burnt Mill, Elizabeth Way, Harlow, CM20 2HX England
Tel: +44 (0)1279 82 89 82   Fax: +44 (0)1279 82 89 83
sales@fabermusic.com   www.fabermusic.com

Contents

1. Presto

Leoš Janáček
(1854–1928)

RECITAL REPERTOIRE FOR CELLISTS

Selected and edited by Julian Lloyd Webber and Simon Nicholls
for Cello and Piano · Book One

Contents

© 1987 by Faber Music Ltd
First published in 1987 by Faber Music Ltd
3 Queen Square London WC1N 3AU
Music engraved by Allan Hill
Printed in England by Caligraving Ltd
All rights reserved

ISBN 0-571-50793-X

To buy Faber Music publications or to find out about the full range of titles available
please contact your local music retailer or Faber Music sales enquiries:

Faber Music Limited, Burnt Mill, Elizabeth Way, Harlow, CM20 2HX England
Tel: +44 (0)1279 82 89 82   Fax: +44 (0)1279 82 89 83
sales@fabermusic.com   www.fabermusic.com

FABER ***ff*** MUSIC

1. Presto

Leoš Janáček
(1854–1928)

* The cello part in bs.85–138 is written an octave higher in the MS

4

2. Ridente la calma
(Peace and Content)

W.A. Mozart*, arr. S.N.
(1756–1791)

* *Ridente la calma* is Mozart's rewriting of *Il caro mio bene* by
Josef Mysliveček (1737–1781)

** Suggested appoggiatura

3. Largo
(from Sonata, op.65)

Fryderyk Chopin
(1810–1849)

4. Cake-walk

Simon Nicholls

5. Adagio and Presto
(from Sinfonia in F)

G.B. Pergolesi
(1710–1736)

6. Scherzo
(from String Trio, op.77b)

Max Reger, arr. S.N.
(1873–1916)

* The cello part in bs.85–138 is written an octave higher in the MS

2. Ridente la calma
(Peace and Content)

W.A. Mozart*, arr. S.N.
(1756–1791)

* *Ridente la calma* is Mozart's rewriting of *Il caro mio bene* by
Josef Mysliveček (1737–1781)

** Suggested appoggiatura

3. Largo
(from Sonata, op.65)

Fryderyk Chopin
(1810–1849)

4. Cake-walk

Simon Nicholls

5. Adagio and Presto

(from Sinfonia in F)

G.B. Pergolesi, realised S.N.
(1710–1736)

6. Scherzo

(from String Trio, op.77b)

Max Reger, arr. S.N.
(1873–1916)

CELLO TEACHING MATERIAL
FROM FABER MUSIC

PAT LEGG

Superstudies

*Really easy original studies for
the young player*

BOOK 1 ISBN 0-571-51378-6
BOOK 2 ISBN 0-571-51445-6

PAT LEGG and ALAN GOUT

Learning the Tenor Clef

*Progressive Studies and Pieces
for Cellists*

ISBN 0-571-51917-2

MARY COHEN

Superduets

*Fantastic cello duets
for beginners*

BOOK 1 ISBN 0-571-51891-5
BOOK 2 ISBN 0-571-51892-3

PAT LEGG and ALAN GOUT

Thumb Position for
Beginners

*Easy pieces for cello duet
and cello/piano*

ISBN 0-571-51801-X

MARY COHEN

Technique takes off!

*14 intermediate studies
for solo cello*

ISBN 0-571-51420-0

PAT LEGG and ALAN GOUT

Thumb Position Repertoire

*Intermediate pieces
for cello and piano*

ISBN 0-571-51802-8

**POLLY WATERFIELD
and GILLIAN LUBACH**

Polytekniks

*Cello duets for musical and
technical accomplishment*

EASY ISBN 0-571-51490-1
INTERMEDIATE ISBN 0-571-51499-5

PAT LEGG

Position Jazz

*Up-beat, original pieces
for cello duet*

ISBN 0-571-51144-9

FABER *ff* MUSIC

UNBEATEN TRACKS

8 contemporary pieces for Cello and Piano

Edited by Steven Isserlis

ISBN 0-571-51976-8

Unbeaten Tracks for cello brings the diverse world of contemporary music within the reach of the less-experienced player (around Grades 4 to 7). The eight pieces in the volume – all specially commissioned by world-famous cellist Steven Isserlis – are written in an array of musical styles by some of today's most talented composers.

Steven Isserlis: 'I am delighted with this collection of weird and wonderful pieces – a collection that I hope will come to be viewed as staple repertoire for cello students, as well as fascinating encores for professionals (I'm already performing several of them regularly). One of the qualities that I find most appealing in this volume is the variety of musical personalities that shine through each offering …'

Carl Davis	*Elegy*
Lowell Liebermann	*Album leaf, Op.66*
Olli Mustonen	*Frogs dancing on water lilies*
John Woolrich	*Cantilena*
Julian Jacobson	*Hip hip bourrée*
Mark-Anthony Turnage	*Vocalise*
David Matthews	*Tango flageoletto*
Steven Isserlis	*The haunted house*

FABER *ff* MUSIC